MAKING YOUR
HOME
a haven

A 4-WEEK BIBLE STUDY
by Courtney Joseph

Welcome to Good Morning Girls! We are so glad you are joining us.

God created us to walk with Him, to know Him, and to be loved by Him. He is our living well, and when we drink from the water He continually provides, His living water will change the entire course of our lives.

Jesus said: "Whoever drinks of the water that I will give him will never be thirsty again. The water that I will give him will become in him a spring of water welling up to eternal life." ~ John 4:14 (ESV)

So let's begin.

The method we use here at GMG is called the **SOAK** method.

- ❏ **S**—The S stands for *Scripture*—Read the chapter for the day. Then choose 1-2 verses and write them out word for word. (There is no right or wrong choice—just let the Holy Spirit guide you.)

- ❏ **O**—The O stands for *Observation*—Look at the verse or verses you wrote out. Write 1 or 2 observations. What stands out to you? What do you learn about the character of God from these verses? Is there a promise, command or teaching?

- ❏ **A**—The A stands for *Application*—Personalize the verses. What is God saying to you? How can you apply them to your life? Are there any changes you need to make or an action to take?

- ❏ **K**—The K stands for *Kneeling in Prayer*—Pause, kneel and pray. Confess any sin God has revealed to you today. Praise God for His word. Pray the passage over your own life or someone you love. Ask God to help you live out your applications.

SOAK God's word into your heart and squeeze every bit of nourishment you can out of each day's scripture reading. Soon you will find your life transformed by the renewing of your mind!

Walk with the King!

Courtney

WomenLivingWell.org, GoodMorningGirls.org

Join the GMG Community

WomenLivingWell.org | GoodMorningGirls.org

Facebook.com/WomenLivingwell | Facebook.com/GoodMorningGirlsWLW

Instagram.com/WomenLivingWell   #WomenLivingWell

#MakingYourHomeAHaven

GMG Bible Coloring Chart

COLORS	KEYWORDS
PURPLE	God, Jesus, Holy Spirit, Saviour, Messiah
PINK	women of the Bible, family, marriage, parenting, friendship, relationships
RED	love, kindness, mercy, compassion, peace, grace
GREEN	faith, obedience, growth, fruit, salvation, fellowship, repentance
YELLOW	worship, prayer, praise, doctrine, angels, miracles,power of God, blessings
BLUE	wisdom, teaching, instruction, commands
ORANGE	prophecy, history, times, places, kings, genealogies, people, numbers, covenants, vows, visions, oaths, future
BROWN/GRAY	Satan, sin, death, hell, evil, idols, false teachers, hypocrisy, temptation

TABLE OF CONTENTS

INTRODUCTION

Welcome to the *Making Your Home a Haven* Bible Study! Ten years ago, I began this series on-line at WomenLivingWell.org. Never could I have imagined how much it would resonate with so many women around the world. I pray this study blesses you in the same way!

If you have been feeling disconnected from God or if you have a desire to go deeper in your walk with the Lord, then this study is for you.

God's pace is much slower than this world's pace.

We must slow down to catch up with God.

We must create calm moments in our day because it's in the unhurried moments that we can clearly see and hear the voice of God.

This Bible Study is going to help you slow down. It is going to force you to pause every day and enter into the presence of our Almighty God through thanksgiving, meditation, prayer and fasting.

Self-care is a very popular concept these days, but I believe that soul care IS self-care. So, let's take care of our souls by intentionally creating a physical environment, as well as a spiritual environment, in our homes that brings us closer to God. As a result, we will experience peace and a sense of calmness inside our souls, no matter what we are facing.

Each week, I will provide for you a practical challenge of something I do in my home that makes it more of a haven. I hope you will take the challenges. They do make a difference!

Each weekday, we will pause, give thanks, pray and meditate on God's Word through SOAKing in the daily scripture reading for the day.

Also, online at WomenLivingWell.org you will find four videos, one per week, that correspond with the scriptures we are studying.

I encourage you to give yourself permission to not have your to-do list all checked off in order for you to slow down and catch up with God.

David writes in Psalm 42:1, 2:

> [1]*"As the deer pants for streams of water,*
> *so my soul pants for you, my God.*
> [2]*My soul thirsts for God, for the living God.*
> *When can I go and meet with God?"*

I pray that your time spent in God's Word will bless your soul and quench your thirst and that you will live well, as you drink from the living well, the living words of God. (John 4:13-14)

I can't wait to take this journey with you!

Keep Walking with the King,

Courtney

Week 1: Gratitude

Give thanks to the Lord, for he is good, for his steadfast love endures forever.

Psalm 136:1

Jesus died on the cross and rose again for the forgiveness of our sins. Through our faith in Jesus, we have a personal relationship with Him. Our God is personal. Never forget that! He is our creator and He loves us. He knows exactly what is best for us. So, He tells us in His Word to give thanks.

Giving thanks is an important spiritual discipline that helps open our eyes to the good gifts that God has generously given to us each day.

Interestingly, it is also scientifically proven that listing the things we are grateful for improves our relationships, our mood, our sleep, our hopefulness, our resiliency and our physical and psychological health.

So many times, we wonder what God's will is for our lives and right in 1 Thessalonians 5:18, God clearly tells us that ***"giving thanks in all circumstances is the will of God".***

So, let's do it! I am 100% certain we will be blessed.

WEEK 1 CHALLENGE

Go buy an extra-large candle and light your candle every day in your home. Each time the glimmer of the candle catches your eye, stop and pray.

I will be starting my candle in the morning, but you can start yours at dinnertime or whenever is convenient for you. I will be placing mine in the kitchen—the main hub of my home.

{Share your pictures of your candle on Instagram by using the hashtags: #MakingYourHomeAHaven and #WomenLivingWell}

DAY 1

Do not be anxious about anything, but in everything by prayer and supplication with thanksgiving let your requests be made known to God.

Philippians 4:6

Things I Am Grateful for Today:

_____

_____

_____

_____

_____

_____

_____

_____

Things I Am Praying for Today:

_____

_____

_____

_____

_____

_____

_____

_____

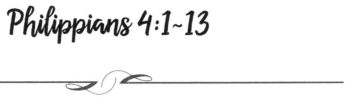

S—The S stands for **Scripture**

O—The O stands for **Observation**

A—The A stands for **Application**

K—The K stands for **Kneeling in Prayer**

DAY 2

Be thankful.

Colossians 3:15

Things I Am Grateful for Today:

_____

_____

_____

_____

_____

_____

_____

_____

Things I Am Praying for Today:

_____

_____

_____

_____

_____

_____

_____

_____

Colossians 3:1-17

S—The S stands for *Scripture*

O—The O stands for *Observation*

A—The A stands for *Application*

K—The K stands for *Kneeling in Prayer*

DAY 3

And he fell on his face at Jesus' feet, giving him thanks.

Luke 17:16

Things I Am Grateful for Today:

_____

_____

_____

_____

_____

_____

_____

_____

Things I Am Praying for Today:

_____

_____

_____

_____

_____

_____

_____

_____

Luke 17:11~19

S—The S stands for **Scripture**

O—The O stands for **Observation**

A—The A stands for **Application**

K—The K stands for **Kneeling in Prayer**

DAY 4

Thanks be to God for his inexpressible gift!

2 Corinthians 9:15

Things I Am Grateful for Today:

_____

_____

_____

_____

_____

_____

_____

Things I Am Praying for Today:

_____

_____

_____

_____

_____

_____

_____

S—The S stands for *Scripture*

O—The O stands for *Observation*

A—The A stands for *Application*

K—The K stands for *Kneeling in Prayer*

DAY 5

*Daniel got down on his knees three times a day and prayed
and gave thanks before his God.*

Daniel 6:10

Things I Am Grateful for Today:

_____

_____

_____

_____

_____

_____

_____

_____

Things I Am Praying for Today:

_____

_____

_____

_____

_____

_____

_____

_____

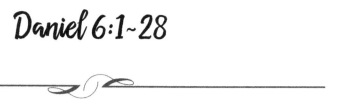

Daniel 6:1~28

S—The S stands for **Scripture**

O—The O stands for **Observation**

A—The A stands for **Application**

K—The K stands for **Kneeling in Prayer**

Week 2: Meditation

This Book of the Law shall not depart from your mouth,
but you shall meditate on it day and night, so that you may be careful
to do according to all that is written in it."

Joshua 1:8

Sometimes I find myself distracted while reading my Bible. If I do not intentionally focus on what I am reading, it is easy for me to forget what I read during my time in His Word. This is why the discipline of meditation is so important.

Meditating on God's Word is more than just reading it. It is taking the time to slowly reflect and think about what the passage means or how the passage applies to our lives. Sometimes it includes committing scripture to memory, so we are able to recall it when temptations and trials come.

David said: *"I have hidden your word in my heart that I might not sin against you." (Psalms 119:11).* **The only way to hide God's Word in our hearts is to read it over and over until it changes our thoughts, shapes our decisions and becomes our standard for living.**

Meditating takes time but it is a vital spiritual discipline that helps us go deeper in our walk with the Lord. Like a sponge, let's sit this week and linger over God's Word and literally soak it in and squeeze all the spiritual nourishment we can out of his Word. I know your soul will be refreshed.

WEEK 2 CHALLENGE

Keep your candle going and add to it soft music every day in your home. Choose worship, classical or another form of peaceful music that helps you focus on the Lord.

My candle and soft music literally change the atmosphere of my home. While the rest of my home may be messy, my candles keep on burning and my soft music keeps on playing. Morning, noon and night they serve me. My candle serves me with a flickering warm light, a pleasant scent, and a reminder to turn to God as my source of strength and help. My music serves me with a soothing sound. They don't make messes, they don't need managed, they just simply bless me and my family. I hope it blesses you too.

{Share your pictures of your favorite Worship CD or playlist on Instagram by using the hashtags: #MakingYourHomeAHaven and #WomenLivingWell }

DAY 1

His delight is in the law of the LORD,
and on his law he meditates day and night.

Psalm 1:2

Things I Am Grateful for Today:

_____

_____

_____

_____

_____

_____

_____

_____

Things I Am Praying for Today:

_____

_____

_____

_____

_____

_____

_____

Psalm 1:1-6

S—The S stands for ***Scripture***

O—The O stands for ***Observation***

A—The A stands for ***Application***

K—The K stands for ***Kneeling in Prayer***

DAY 2

Let the words of my mouth and the meditation of my heart be acceptable in your sight, O LORD, my rock and my redeemer.

Psalm 19:14

Things I Am Grateful for Today:

_____

_____

_____

_____

_____

_____

_____

Things I Am Praying for Today:

_____

_____

_____

_____

_____

_____

_____

Psalm 19:1-14

S—The S stands for *Scripture*

O—The O stands for *Observation*

A—The A stands for *Application*

K—The K stands for *Kneeling in Prayer*

DAY 3

You keep him in perfect peace him whose mind is stayed on you,
because he trusts in you.

Isaiah 26:3

Things I Am Grateful for Today:

_____
_____
_____
_____
_____
_____
_____
_____

Things I Am Praying for Today:

_____
_____
_____
_____
_____
_____
_____
_____

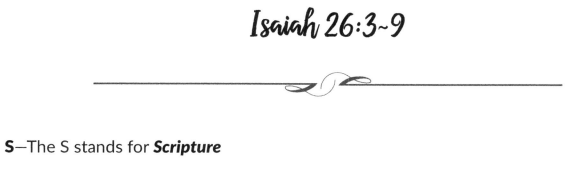

Isaiah 26:3-9

S—The S stands for *Scripture*

O—The O stands for *Observation*

A—The A stands for *Application*

K—The K stands for *Kneeling in Prayer*

DAY 4

This Book of the Law shall not depart from your mouth,
but you shall meditate on it day and night, so that you may be careful to do
according to all that is written in it. For then you will make your way prosperous,
and then you will have good success.

Joshua 1:8

Things I Am Grateful for Today:

_____

_____

_____

_____

_____

_____

_____

Things I Am Praying for Today:

_____

_____

_____

_____

_____

_____

_____

Joshua 1:1~9

S—The S stands for **Scripture**

O—The O stands for **Observation**

A—The A stands for **Application**

K—The K stands for **Kneeling in Prayer**

DAY 5

I will meditate on your precepts and fix my eyes on your ways.

Psalm 119:15

Things I Am Grateful for Today:

_____

_____

_____

_____

_____

_____

_____

_____

Things I Am Praying for Today:

_____

_____

_____

_____

_____

_____

_____

_____

Psalm 119:1-16

S—The S stands for **Scripture**

O—The O stands for **Observation**

A—The A stands for **Application**

K—The K stands for **Kneeling in Prayer**

Week 3: Prayer

The prayer of a righteous person has great power as it is working.

James 5:16

Finding time to pray is not easy! In the past, I have described prayer as a wrestling match. Have you experienced this? You sit down to pray, and within one minute your brain is distracted? I start thinking about my to-do list, or I get interrupted by the kids or worse, I drift off to sleep! It's like a thousand invisible enemies seem to fill the air the minute I sit down to pray.

One way I fight off the enemy is by continuing to daily light my candle and each time the flicker of the candle catches my eye—I am reminded to pray. Another way I remind myself to pray is to set the alarm on my iPhone. When it goes off, I pause and pray for friends I have committed to pray for or concerns that I want to continually lay down at the Lord's feet. Another solution to my wandering mind is to journal my prayers. For over 30 years, I have kept a prayer journal. Sometimes I write prayer lists and other times I write long letters to God.

I love what Edith Shaeffer has written about the power of journaling. She says: "God has communicated with us in writing. His Word, the Bible...So writing our pleas, our praise, our prayers—this is not a one-sided communication. God will hear, and He will answer... It's a relaxed and protected comforting communication with one's Father, Shepherd, Friend, Counselor and mighty God. He is Personal—and therefore we can speak and write to Him in a personal and intimate communication."

Though it's hard to fit long extended prayer times into our daily lives—it is possible, and it is precious and worth fighting for. Let's make a plan to pray this week! Grab a journal, set your alarms, light your candles, or simply fall on your knees and go to the Lord in prayer. He loves you and He is listening!

WEEK 3 CHALLENGE

Go pick a bouquet of flowers from your garden or a nearby field or buy yourself a small bouquet. Each time you see the flowers, be reminded of God's love and presence with you.

I will be purchasing a small bouquet from my grocery store and placing it in a vase, in my kitchen.

{Share your pictures of your flowers on Instagram by using the hashtags: #MakingYourHomeAHaven and #WomenLivingWell}

DAY 1

And he told them a parable to the effect that they ought always to pray and not lose heart.

Luke 18:1

Things I Am Grateful for Today:

_____

_____

_____

_____

_____

_____

_____

_____

Things I Am Praying for Today:

_____

_____

_____

_____

_____

_____

_____

_____

_____

S—The S stands for **Scripture**

O—The O stands for **Observation**

A—The A stands for **Application**

K—The K stands for **Kneeling in Prayer**

DAY 2

But when you pray, go into your room and shut the door and pray to your Father who is in secret. And your Father who sees in secret will reward you.

Matthew 6:6

Things I Am Grateful for Today:

_____

_____

_____

_____

_____

_____

_____

_____

Things I Am Praying for Today:

_____

_____

_____

_____

_____

_____

_____

_____

_____

Matthew 6:1-18

S—The S stands for **Scripture**

O—The O stands for **Observation**

A—The A stands for **Application**

K—The K stands for **Kneeling in Prayer**

DAY 3

The prayer of a righteous person has great power as it is working.

James 5:16

Things I Am Grateful for Today:

_____

_____

_____

_____

_____

_____

_____

Things I Am Praying for Today:

_____

_____

_____

_____

_____

_____

_____

James 5:12~24

S—The S stands for **Scripture**

O—The O stands for **Observation**

A—The A stands for **Application**

K—The K stands for **Kneeling in Prayer**

DAY 4

Pray without ceasing.

1 Thessalonians 5:17

Things I Am Grateful for Today:

_____

_____

_____

_____

_____

_____

_____

_____

Things I Am Praying for Today:

_____

_____

_____

_____

_____

_____

_____

_____

1 Thessalonians 5:12~24

S—The S stands for *Scripture*

O—The O stands for *Observation*

A—The A stands for *Application*

K—The K stands for *Kneeling in Prayer*

DAY 5

Praying at all times in the Spirit, with all prayer and supplication.

Ephesians 6:18

Things I Am Grateful for Today:

_____

_____

_____

_____

_____

_____

_____

_____

Things I Am Praying for Today:

_____

_____

_____

_____

_____

_____

_____

_____

Ephesians 6:10~20

S—The S stands for **_Scripture_**

O—The O stands for **_Observation_**

A—The A stands for **_Application_**

K—The K stands for **_Kneeling in Prayer_**

Week 4: Fasting

16 "And when you fast, do not look gloomy like the hypocrites, for they disfigure their faces that their fasting may be seen by others. Truly, I say to you, they have received their reward. 17 But when you fast, anoint your head and wash your face, 18 that your fasting may not be seen by others but by your Father who is in secret. And your Father who sees in secret will reward you.

Matthew 6:16-18

This week is not going to be easy. Fasting is the most difficult spiritual discipline of them all. Fasting is a servant that feeds our soul while we starve our body. **Every time our mind signals "I want food", it's a signal to pray.** Giving up food and coffee from sun down to sun down brings out our soul's deepest struggles. The hope of a bag of chips or a gallon of ice cream to drown out our sorrows is stripped away, and we find ourselves raw before God's throne.

On days of fasting for me, I have minimal computer time and texting. Sometimes I do it with a friend, so we will text and email each other encouragement. But otherwise, it's a quiet day. There is nothing and no one to conceal my honest feelings and it is there, before God's throne, that I find time and time again, indeed **God is enough.**

So, here's a few tips as we get started. 1.) Look at your calendar and pick a day where you are home most of the day. 2.) I like to go from sundown to sundown, which means an early supper in the winter time on day 1 but the next evening it is such a joy to break the fast with family! 3.) Fasting is not to impress God or others. Fasting was created by God as a tool to bring us into a closer relationship with him. 4.) Without prayer, fasting is simply a diet. Be sure to commit to praying and meditating. 5.) If you are a mom of little ones, have the kids join in some of your prayer times. Also try to line up quiet activities for them to do so you can break away for pockets of prayer times. I will admit, lunch time and afternoon snack time can be a beast, but you can do it!

Are you hungry for God? As Susan Gregory once said, *"Sometimes you are so hungry, the only way to be fed is to fast."*

WEEK 4 CHALLENGE

Seek out a place of solitude to pray. Get alone with God outside or in your home. Be still with God and fervently pray. If you are not able to fast from food because you are pregnant or have a medical condition, fast from something else like social media, music, your computer, or television. Use the extra quietness to pray.

DAY 1

When you fast, do not look gloomy like the hypocrites, for they disfigure their faces that their fasting may be seen by others.

Matthew 6:16

Things I Am Grateful for Today:

_____

_____

_____

_____

_____

_____

_____

_____

Things I Am Praying for Today:

_____

_____

_____

_____

_____

_____

_____

_____

_____

Matthew 6:16~18

S—The S stands for **Scripture**

O—The O stands for **Observation**

A—The A stands for **Application**

K—The K stands for **Kneeling in Prayer**

DAY 2

Then Jesus was led up by the Spirit into the wilderness to be tempted by the devil.
And after fasting forty days and forty nights, he was hungry.

Matthew 4:1, 2

Things I Am Grateful for Today:

_____

_____

_____

_____

_____

_____

_____

_____

Things I Am Praying for Today:

_____

_____

_____

_____

_____

_____

_____

_____

S—The S stands for *Scripture*

O—The O stands for *Observation*

A—The A stands for *Application*

K—The K stands for *Kneeling in Prayer*

DAY 3

*Go, gather all the Jews to be found in Susa, and hold a fast on my behalf,
and do not eat or drink for three days, night or day.
I and my young women will also fast as you do. Then I will go to the king,
though it is against the law, and if I perish, I perish."*

Esther 4:16

Things I Am Grateful for Today:

_____

_____

_____

_____

_____

_____

_____

Things I Am Praying for Today:

_____

_____

_____

_____

_____

_____

_____

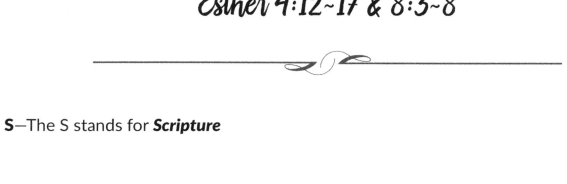

Esther 4:12~17 & 8:3~8

S—The S stands for **Scripture**

O—The O stands for **Observation**

A—The A stands for **Application**

K—The K stands for **Kneeling in Prayer**

DAY 4

Test your servants for ten days: let us be given vegetables
to eat and water to drink.

Daniel 1:12

Things I Am Grateful for Today:

_____

_____

_____

_____

_____

_____

_____

Things I Am Praying for Today:

_____

_____

_____

_____

_____

_____

_____

_____

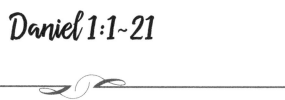
S—The S stands for ***Scripture***

O—The O stands for ***Observation***

A—The A stands for ***Application***

K—The K stands for ***Kneeling in Prayer***

DAY 5

*Anna did not depart from the temple,
worshiping with fasting and prayer night and day.*

Luke 2:37

Things I Am Grateful for Today:

_____

_____

_____

_____

_____

_____

_____

Things I Am Praying for Today:

_____

_____

_____

_____

_____

_____

_____

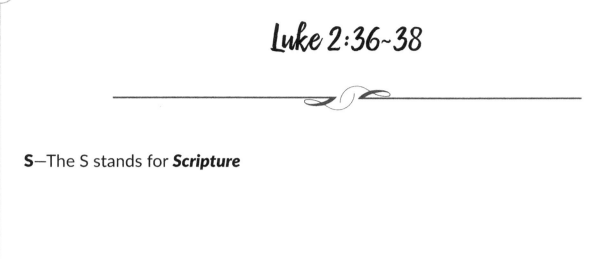

Luke 2:36~38

S—The S stands for **Scripture**

O—The O stands for **Observation**

A—The A stands for **Application**

K—The K stands for **Kneeling in Prayer**

Video Notes

(go to WomenLivingWell.org to find the weekly corresponding videos)

Made in the USA
Columbia, SC
04 November 2019